Usborne
Wipe-Clean
Garden
Activities

Illustrated by Dania Florino

Designed by Laura Hammonds

Written by Kirsteen Robson

Use your wipe-clean pen to do all the activities in this fun-filled book.

6 7 8 9 10

Springtime

Use the pen to
draw more leaves
on this tree.

Becca

Draw over the
dots to show Becca
Bear where to cut
the grass.

Count the eggs in each nest, then trace over the numbers below.

4

3

2

Draw lines between the birds that match each other.

Can you find and circle 4 differences between these wheelbarrows?

In the pond

Use the pen to show Happy the way to swim
through the water to his friend Hoppy.

Happy

Draw over the
dots to finish the
fountain.

Write an X above the dragonfly that does not match the others.

Hoppy

Sally

7 8 9 2 3 6 1 10 5 4

Connect the dots to draw a shell for Sally Snail.

Summer days

Follow the lines to find out which butterfly will land on the flower.

Becca

Draw over the dots to help Becca Bear water the flowers.

Circle 5 differences between these two flowerbeds.

Connect the dots to
finish the shed.

Draw the other
half of each
butterfly.

Trace over the dots to
finish these flowers.

Inside the shed

Draw the other half of these garden tools.

Trace over the numbers to see how many leaves each plant needs. Then, draw on the missing leaves.

4   6   5

Draw 5 straight lines to finish the spider's web.

Find and circle 6 spiders.

Decorate the watering can with stripes and zigzags and finish the handles.

Seeds

The vegetable patch

Find 6 differences between Sandy and Seb scarecrow.

Draw over the dots to finish the Sun.

Sandy

Seb

Draw lines between the vegetables that match each other.

Connect the dots to finish
Becca Bear's greenhouse.

Draw 5 more tomatoes.

Follow the lines and see which
rabbit will eat the most plants.

A garden party

Draw 3 more puffs
of smoke above
the barbecue grill.

Finish the gate
by drawing
over the dots.

Draw lines
between the plates
of food that match
each other.

Draw over the dots to finish the plants. Draw more leaves so each plant has 4.

Find and circle 5 balls.

Draw the missing part of the hose, with 3 loops in it.

In the orchard

Trace over the numbers to see how many apples each tree needs. Then, draw on the missing apples.

7

8

Use the pen to show Becca Bear the way to Felix Fox.

Becca

Draw over the dots to finish 2 trees. How many apples are on each tree?

Felix

Write an X under the bee that does not match the others.

1 10

2

3

9

4

8

5

7

6

Connect the dots to see what fruit is hanging on the branch.

Windy days

Draw over the dots to see
what is hanging on the line.

Find and circle 8 blue socks.

Count the leaves in
each pile, then trace
over the numbers.

8

9

10

Draw 10 more leaves
whirling in the wind.

Finish Dexter
Dog's swing by
drawing over
the dots.

Dexter

Follow the strings
to see who is flying
each kite.

After dark

Spot 4 differences between Ollie and Olga Owl.

Ollie

Olga

Find and circle 7 moths.

Write an X under the baby hedgehog that does not match the others.

Finish the Moon by drawing over the dots.

Draw 1 missing wing on 3 bats.

Connect the dots to finish drawing the cat.

5
6
7
4
8
3
9
2
1
10

Playing in the snow

Draw over the dots to help
Felix Fox finish his snowman.

Felix

Use the pen to show Cerys
Cat which way to roll her
snowball to Ricky Raccoon.

Cerys

Find and circle 9 birds.

Spot 5 differences between these snowmen.

Ricky

Becca

Draw 6 more of Becca's footprints in the snow.

Draw over the dots to finish the bird table.

Usborne

Wipe-Clean

Garden Activities

This fun book is a perfect way for young children to develop their counting, observation and pen control skills.

CE

£5.99
CAD$10.95

JFMAMJ ASOND/19
05733/1
Made with paper from a sustainable source.

WARNING! Not suitable for children under 36 months because of small parts. Choking hazard.

ATTENTION! Ne convient pas aux enfants de moins de 36 mois en raison des petites pièces. Risque de suffocation par ingestion.

Ink from pen may not be washable.
L'encre du feutre ne s'efface pas toujours au lavage.

ISBN 978-1-4749-1900-5

KR-938-357

9 781474 919005

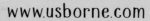

Usborne Publishing Ltd., Usborne House, 83–85 Saffron Hill, London EC1N 8RT, England. Printed in China.
First published in 2017, www.usborne.com © 2017 Usborne Publishing Ltd. The name Usborne and the devices ♀⊕ are Trade Marks of